THE GIRL WITH CURLY HAIR

PRESENTS

THE 1ST COMIC BOOK

ALIS ROWE

Lonely Mind Books
London

Copyrighted Material

First published in 2013
by Lonely Mind Books
London

Copyright © Alis Rowe 2013

All rights reserved. No part of this publication may be reproduced in any material form (including photocopying or storing it in any medium by electronic means and whether or not transiently or incidentally to some other use of this publication) without written permission of the copyright owner except in accordance with the provisions of the Copyright, Designs and Patents Act 1988 or under the terms of a licence issued by the Copyright Licensing Agency Ltd, 90 Tottenham Court Road, London, England W1T 4LP. Applications for the copyright owner's written permission to reproduce any part of this publication should be addressed to the publisher.

Warning: The doing of an unauthorised act in relation to a copyright work may result in both a civil claim for damages and criminal prosecution.

Printed and bound in the UK by Short Run Press
Short Run Press
Bittern Road
Sowton Industrial Estate
Exeter EX2 7LW

ISBN 978-0-9562693-1-7

For people with Asperger's Syndrome and their Neurotypical families and friends

and

my Facebook friends

hello

These comic strips are all very real. They are things that happen to me on a daily basis. I created this book because I wanted others to see into the world of Asperger's Syndrome, including the what, why and how I experience life. Having read this book, my neurotypical mother made the following remark:

"I don't know how you get through every day!"

which really made me think. She hit the nail on the head, so to speak. What might be small challenges for neurotypicals, are very big challenges for people like me. This book recreates everyday situations in a colourful, thought-provoking and sometimes funny way - I wanted it to be an engaging read for everyone.

I hope this book helps both the NT and the AS understand a bit better how one another's mind works.

Some of the comic strips contain more subtleties than you might initially see. For example, notice how the neurotypical refers to time in a simple way, e.g. 6 o' clock or 6pm. In contrast, The Girl with the Curly Hair refers to time as accurately as possible, including minutes, e.g. 6.00pm. It is my intention to show how exact life is for people with Asperger's Syndrome, which is why we often come across as being a bit rigid or inflexible.

I hope you enjoy this book.

Alis aka The Girl with the Curly Hair

Contents

The single bed

SPACE FOR YOUR NOTES...

Why marry?

SPACE FOR YOUR NOTES...

Extra fillings

SPACE FOR YOUR NOTES...

THE GIRL WITH THE CURLY HAIR

AND HER NEUROTYPICAL PARTNER HAVE BOUGHT

SANDWICHES FROM THE SANDWICH BAR.
THEY'VE ADDED EXTRAS SHE HAD NOT ASKED FOR.

Tea teasing

SPACE FOR YOUR NOTES...

The night club

SPACE FOR YOUR NOTES...

THE GIRL WITH THE CURLY HAIR

IS AT A PARTY WITH HER NEUROTYPICAL FRIENDS. FUN? NO, IT'S OVERWHELMING.

Class is cancelled

SPACE FOR YOUR NOTES...

THE GIRL WITH THE CURLY HAIR

ARRIVES AT COLLEGE, ONLY TO FIND OUT HER CLASS HAS BEEN CANCELLED.

THE NEUROTYPICAL STUDENTS ARE PLEASANTLY SURPRISED. SHE IS NOT.

Cuddling the cat

SPACE FOR YOUR NOTES...

THE GIRL WITH THE CURLY HAIR

IS STROKING HER CAT AFTER A STRESSFUL DAY.
ANIMALS ARE EASIER TO RELATE TO THAN PEOPLE.

The office lunch

SPACE FOR YOUR NOTES...

THE GIRL WITH THE CURLY HAIR

IS AT WORK. AT 12PM, THE BOSS ANNOUNCES THE WHOLE TEAM IS GOING OUT FOR LUNCH.

WHAT OTHERS AGREE TO AT A DROP OF A HAT, IS STRESSFUL FOR HER.

BUT I'VE ALREADY GOT MY CHICKEN AND SWEETCORN SANDWICH THAT I BROUGHT FROM HOME.

I DO NOT LIKE HAVING TO EXPLAIN ALL THE TIME, WHY I ONLY DRINK WATER.

I REALLY NEED TO FINISH THIS WORK.

I CAN'T FACE ANY EXTRA SOCIALISING. JUST BEING IN THE OFFICE IS TOO MUCH FOR ME.

DOES THIS MEAN I HAVE TO STAY LATER TO MAKE UP FOR THE TIME? MY EVENING WILL BE RUINED.

I ALREADY KNOW I WON'T WANT ANYTHING IN THE RESTAURANT.

BUT I LIKE TO EAT AT 1.00PM. I'M NOT HUNGRY UNTIL 1.00PM.

IF I HAVE TO STAY LATER AT WORK TONIGHT, DINNER WILL BE TOO LATE. I'LL MISS MY FAVOURITE TV SHOW. EVERYTHING IS RUINED!

Butterflies and weightlifting

SPACE FOR YOUR NOTES...

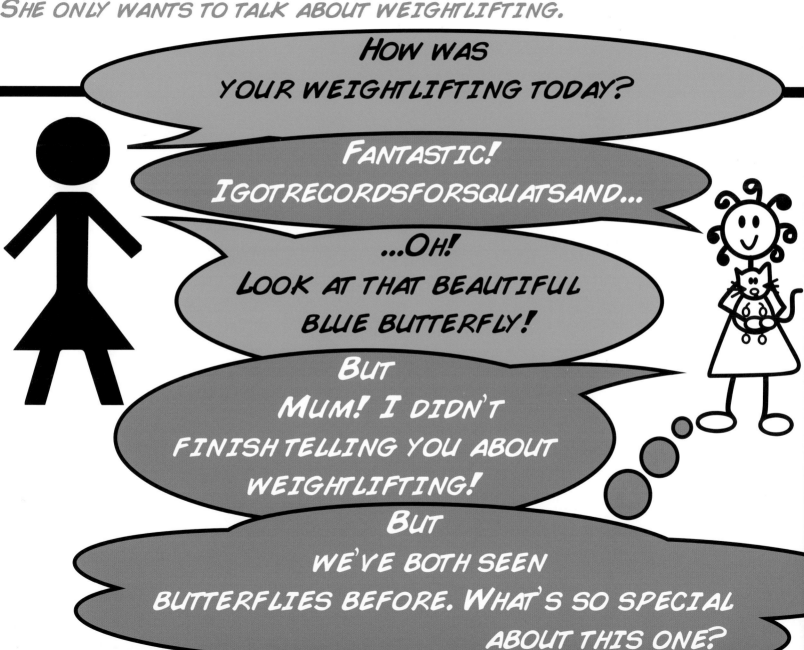

The baby in the cafe

SPACE FOR YOUR NOTES...

Clothes shopping

SPACE FOR YOUR NOTES...

Going to the park

SPACE FOR YOUR NOTES...

The heatwave

SPACE FOR YOUR NOTES...

Flushed

SPACE FOR YOUR NOTES...

Being close

SPACE FOR YOUR NOTES...

THE GIRL WITH THE CURLY HAIR AND HER NEUROTYPICAL PARTNER ARE HAVING SOME INTIMACY TIME.

THEY BOTH LOVE THEIR TIME TOGETHER.

Back from holiday

SPACE FOR YOUR NOTES...

THE GIRL WITH THE CURLY HAIR AND HER NEUROTYPICAL SISTER ARRIVE HOME FROM FRANCE. DAD ASKS HOW IT WENT.

THEY ENJOYED DIFFERENT ASPECTS OF THE HOLIDAY.

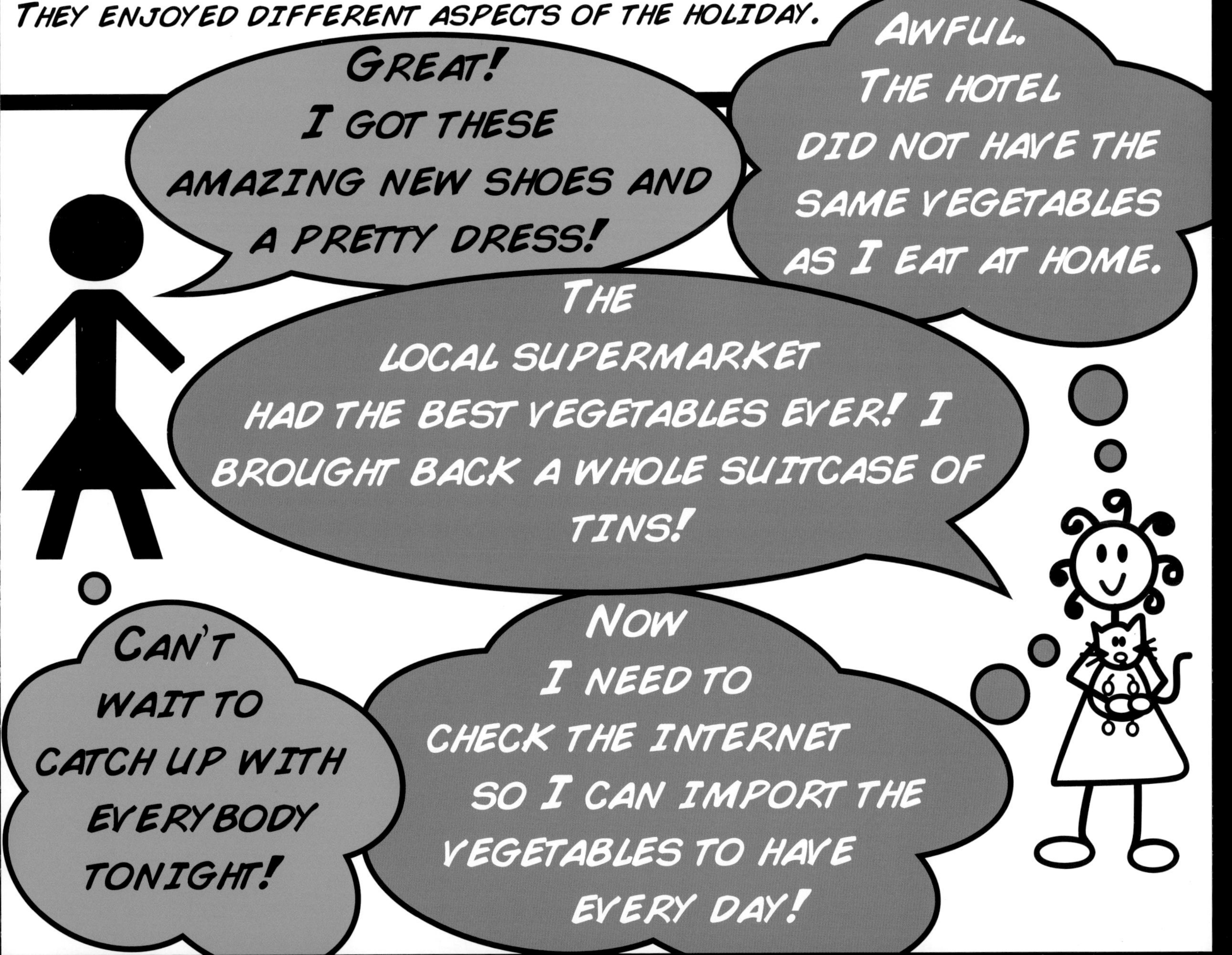

Specifically tea

SPACE FOR YOUR NOTES...

Good morning

SPACE FOR YOUR NOTES...

The Girl with the Curly Hair

and her neurotypical colleague arrive at work. Social niceties are confusing. She says what she's supposed to.

Ponytail

SPACE FOR YOUR NOTES...

THE GIRL WITH THE CURLY HAIR

IS WAITING FOR HER MUM WHO HAS JUST FINISHED AT THE GYM.

APPEARANCES CAN BE CONFUSING.

The haircut

SPACE FOR YOUR NOTES...

THE GIRL WITH THE CURLY HAIR

IS HAVING HER HAIR CUT ON A SATURDAY AFTERNOON.

SOCIAL CHAT MAKES HER PUT ON HER MASK.

Buying ice cream

SPACE FOR YOUR NOTES...

THE GIRL WITH THE CURLY HAIR

ASKS HER DAD TO BUY A LARGE TUB OF HER FAVOURITE ICE CREAM FROM THE SHOP.
HE THINKS HE'S DONE REALLY WELL, BUT SHE IS VERY SPECIFIC IN HER NEEDS.

In the restaurant

SPACE FOR YOUR NOTES...

The Uni party

SPACE FOR YOUR NOTES...

Index